GRAPHIC SCIENCE

ADVENTURES IN

SOUND

WITH MAX AXIOM

SUPER SCIENTIST

Emily Sohn

illustrated by Cynthia Martin and Anne Timmons

www.raintreepublishers.co.uk
Visit our website to find out
more information about
Raintree books.

To order:
☎ Phone +44 (0) 1865 888066
🖹 Fax +44 (0) 1865 314091
🖳 Visit www.raintreepublishers.co.uk

Raintree is an imprint of Capstone Global Library Limited, a company incorporated in England and
Wales having its registered office at 7 Pilgrim Street, London EC4V 6LB
Registered company number: 6695882

"Raintree" is a registered trademark of Pearson Education Limited, under licence to Capstone Global
Library Limited

Text © Capstone Press 2008
First published by Capstone Press in 2008
First published in hardback in the United Kingdom by Capstone Global Library in 2010
The moral rights of the proprietor have been asserted.

ISBN 978 1 406 21455 0 (hardback)
14 13 12 11 10

British Library Cataloguing in Publication Data
Sohn, Emily
Sound. -- (Graphic science)
534-dc22
A full catalogue record for this book is available from the British Library.

Art Director and Designer: Bob Lentz
Cover Artist: Tod Smith
Colourist: Michael Kelleher
UK Editor: Diyan Leake
UK Production: Alison Parsons
Originated by Capstone Global Library
Printed and bound in China by South China Printing Company Limited

Acknowledgements
The publisher would like to thank the following for permission to reproduce copyright material:
Capstone Press, p. 8 bottom (Scott Thoms)

Disclaimer
All the Internet addresses (URLs) given in this book were valid at the time of going to press.
However, due to the dynamic nature of the Internet, some addresses may have changed, or sites may
have changed or ceased to exist since publication. While the publisher regrets any inconvenience this
may cause readers, no responsibility for any such changes can be accepted by the publisher.

CONTENTS

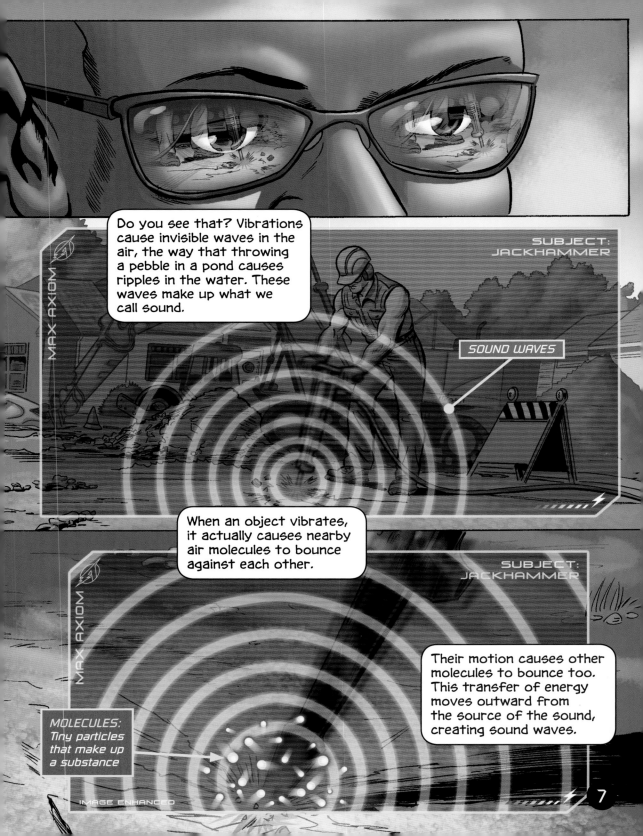

Of course, some sounds are louder than others. The difference is called intensity.

TWEET!
TWEET!
TWEET!

TATATATAT!

Stronger vibrations are more intense. They cause louder sounds.

Loudness is also called volume. The higher the volume, the louder the sound.

PUTT
PUTT
PUTT

IDLE ON OFF

I have a job to do. Please, leave me alone.

PUTT
PUTT
PUTT
PUTT

THE HUMAN LARYNX

ACCESS GRANTED: MAX AXIOM

EPIGLOTTIS
VOCAL CORDS
LARYNX
TRACHEA

Inside your throat, your larynx allows you to talk, sing, and make other noises. Inside the larynx, two muscles called vocal cords squeeze together and vibrate as air passes by them. The faster they vibrate, the higher your voice sounds. Your tongue and lips shape the sounds you make.

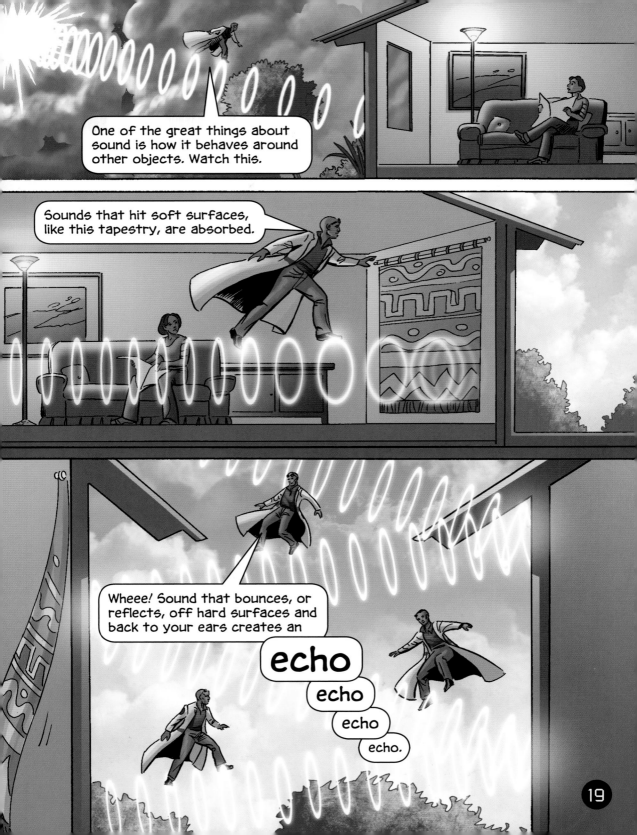

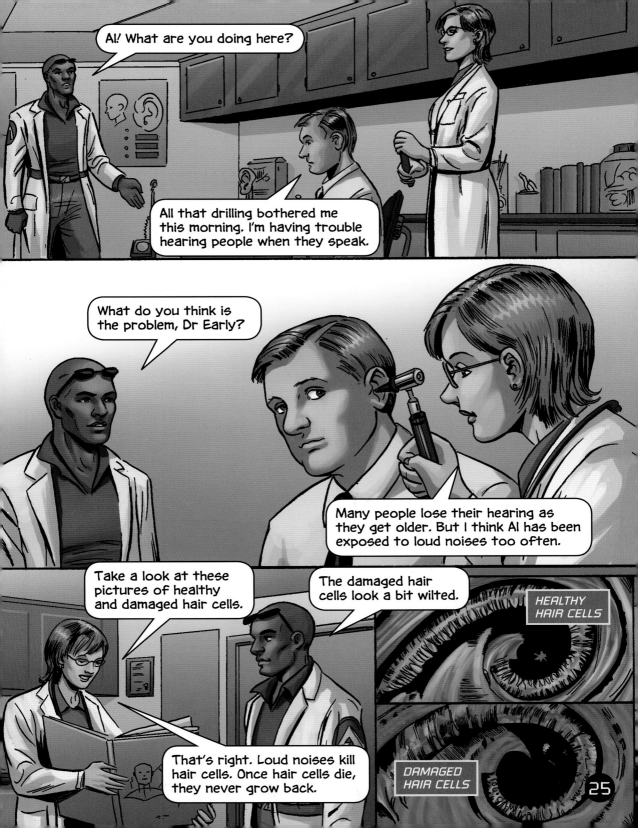

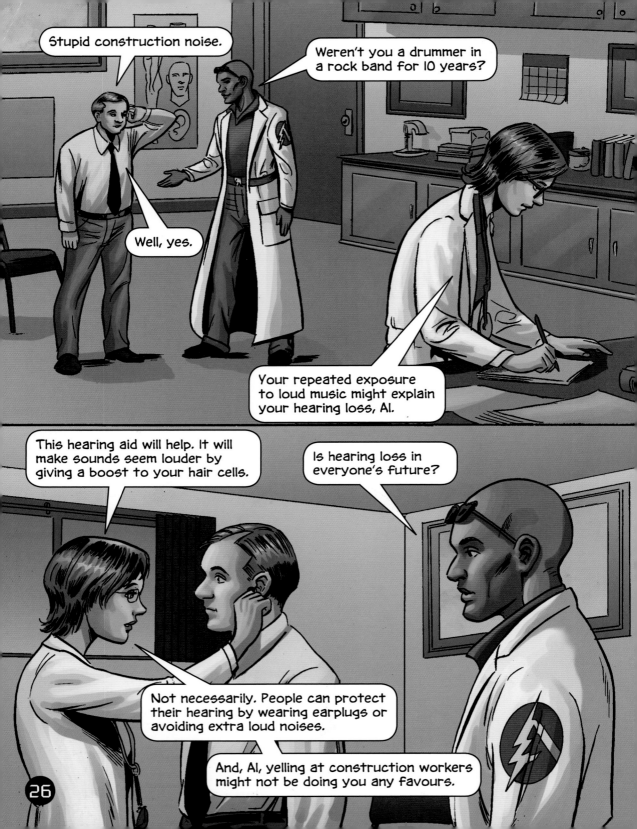

MORE ABOUT SOUND

Sound travels faster through solids than through gases and liquids. Why? Because the molecules in solids are packed closer together. The closer the molecules, the faster the sound waves travel from one molecule to the next. A sound travels 1,240 kilometres (770 miles) per hour through air. It speeds through steel at about 18,716 kilometres (11,630 miles) per hour.

Most bats use echolocation to hunt. As they fly, bats release high-pitched sounds that bounce off objects all around them. The bats use the echoes they hear to locate and determine the size of insects fluttering nearby.

The hammer, anvil, and stirrup are the smallest bones in the human body. They are the same size now as they were the day you were born. All together, they could fit on a penny.

Ear wax helps keep your ears clean. As wax forms inside the ear canal, it clings to dirt particles. Eventually, the wax works its way out of the ear, carrying the dirt along with it.

The liquid in the cochlea does more than just magnify vibrations. It also plays a role in balance and helps your body know what is up and what is down.

Elephants use infrasound, or sound below the range of human hearing, to talk to each other. They can use rumbling sounds as low as 5 Hz to communicate.

A cricket's hearing organs are located just below the knees of its front legs. A cicada's hearing organ is on its abdomen.

 Scientists measure the loudness, or volume, of sounds in decibels (dB). A whisper measures about 20 dB, while normal talking is 60 dB. A jet measures about 120 dB and a firecracker exploding is about 140 dB. Any sound above 85 dB can cause hearing damage if listened to for too long. At close range, noise levels above 140 dB cause immediate hearing damage.

 Blue whales are the loudest animals on earth. Their calls have measured 188 dB and can be heard from hundreds of miles away.

MORE ABOUT

SUPER SCIENTIST

Real name: Maxwell Axiom
Height: 1.86 m (6ft 1 in.)
Weight: 87 kg (13 st. 10 lb.)
Eyes: Brown   **Hair:** None

Super capabilities: Super intelligence; able to shrink to the size of an atom; sunglasses give X-ray vision; lab coat allows for travel through time and space.

Origin: Since birth, Max Axiom seemed destined for greatness. His mother, a marine biologist, taught her son about the mysteries of the sea. His father, a nuclear physicist and volunteer park warden, showed Max the wonders of the earth and sky.

One day, while Max was hiking in the hills, a megacharged lightning bolt struck him with blinding fury. When he awoke, he discovered a new-found energy and set out to learn as much about science as possible. He travelled the globe studying every aspect of the subject. Then he was ready to share his knowledge and new identity with the world. He had become Max Axiom, Super Scientist.

Glossary

absorb soak up

cochlea spiral-shaped part of the ear that helps send sound messages to the brain

decibel unit for measuring the volume of sounds

eardrum thin piece of skin stretched tight like a drum inside the ear; the eardrum vibrates when sound waves strike it.

echolocation the process of using sounds and echoes to locate objects. Bats use echolocation to find food.

energy ability to do work, such as moving things or giving heat or light

frequency the number of sound waves that pass a location in a certain amount of time

hertz unit for measuring the frequency of sound wave vibrations. One hertz equals one sound wave per second.

molecule two or more atoms of the same or different elements that have bonded. A molecule is the smallest part of a compound that can be divided without a chemical change.

pitch highness or lowness of a sound; low pitches have low frequencies and high pitches have high frequencies.

reflect bounce off an object

refract bend when passing through a material at an angle

vibration fast movement back and forth

FIND OUT MORE

Books

Feel the Noise!: Sound Energy, Anna Claybourne (Raintree, 2006)

Secrets of the Deep: Marine Biologists (Scientists at Work series), Mike Unwin (Heinemann, 2007)

Sound: Listen Up! (Science in Your Life series), Wendy Sadler (Raintree, 2005)

Websites

http://www.naturesongs.com/
Listen to the sounds of animals, weather, oceans, and much more.

http://www.eureka.org.uk
Click on "Fun stuff", then on "Games", and choose "Good Vibrations" for a fun way to find out how sound travels at different speeds through different materials.

INDEX